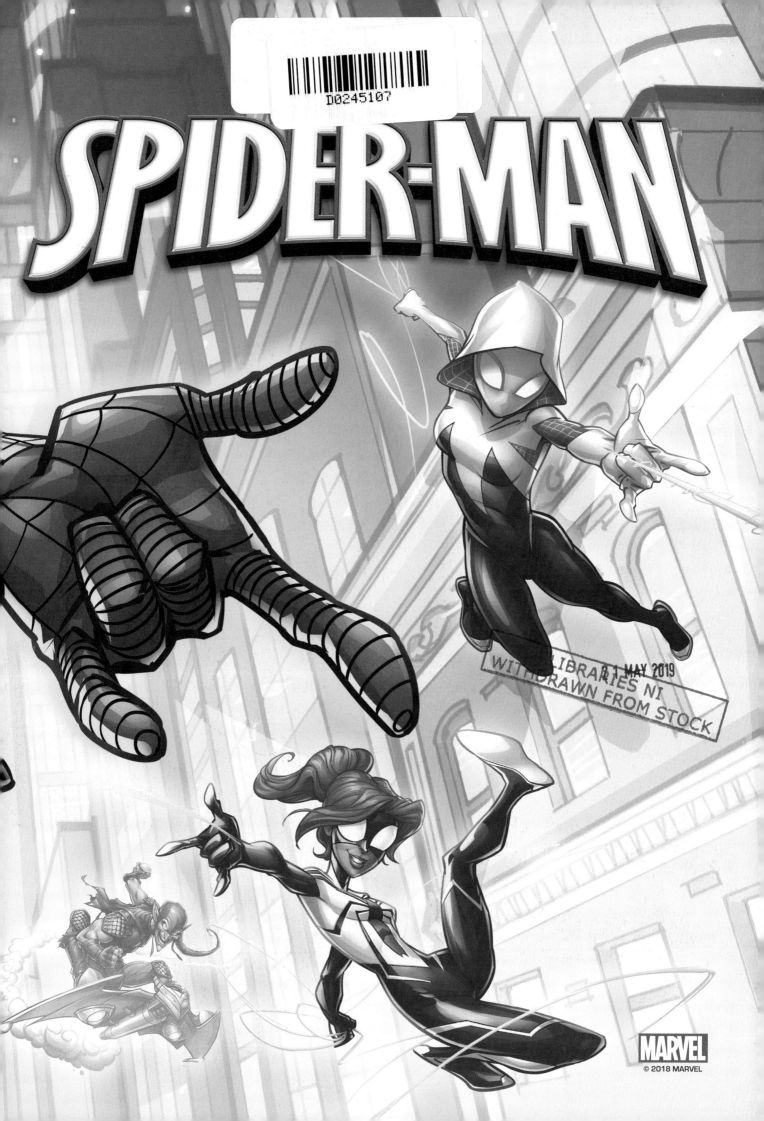

MARVEL
SPIDER-MAN

COMIC STRIP...

INSIDE...

© 2018 MARVEL

FSC
www.fsc.org
MIX
Paper from
responsible sources
FSC® C005461

Spider-Man Annual 2019 is published by Panini Publishing, a division of Panini UK Limited. Office of publication: Panini UK Ltd. Brockbourne House, 77 Mount Ephraim, Tunbridge Wells, Kent, TN4 8BS. MARVEL, and all related characters: TM & © 2018 Marvel Entertainment, LLC and its subsidiaries. Licensed by Marvel Characters B.V. www.marvel.com. All rights reserved. No similarity between any of the names, characters, persons and/or institutions in this edition with those of any living or dead person or institution is intended, and any such similarity which may exist is purely coincidental. This publication may not be sold, except by authorised dealers, and is sold subject to the condition that it shall not be sold or distributed with any part of its cover or markings removed, nor in a mutilated condition. This publication is produced under licence from Marvel Characters, Inc. through Panini S.p.A. Printed in Italy by Rotolito S.p.A. ISBN: 978-1-84653-241-2

£7.99

SENSE

SPIDER FILE

READ ON TO FIND OUT 10 AMAZING FACTS ABOUT SPIDEY'S EARLY WARNING SYSTEM, HIS SPIDER-SENSE!

LOOKOUT
THE SPIDER-SENSE HELPS KEEP SPIDEY'S IDENTITY SECRET, BY WARNING HIM OF OBSERVERS WHEN HE'S CHANGING.

TINGLING
SPIDEY'S SPIDER-SENSE IS A TINGLING SENSATION AT THE BACK OF HIS SKULL THAT ALERTS HIM TO PERSONAL DANGER.

HIDDEN DANGER
THE SENSE CAN ALSO TELL SPIDEY THE DIRECTION OF THE DANGER, SO HE CAN DISCOVER HIDDEN WEAPONS AND ENEMIES.

EVER GET THE FEELING YOU'VE BEEN HAD, SPIDER-MAN?

THE CHAMELEON!

LOUSY FINK GOT RIGHT UNDER MY RADAR. OR LACK OF IT ANYWAY.

TRACERS
PETER PARKER DESIGNED HIS SPIDER-TRACERS TO BE DETECTABLE BY HIS SPIDER-SENSE.

HOW MUCH?
THE SPIDER-SENSE CAN'T TELL SPIDEY THE TYPE OF DANGER, BUT CAN SHOW HOW SEVERE IT IS.

DUNNO, H.E.R.B.I.E. -- BUT GET READY FOR TROUBLE...

WHOA! SPIDER-SENSE KICKING IN...

WHAT IS WRONG, SPIDER-MAN?

...ATIONAL!

STUNNING
SPIDEY'S SPIDER-SENSE CAN EVEN SAVE HIM WHEN HE IS ASLEEP OR STUNNED.

FLYING HIGH
THE SPIDER-SENSE HELPS SPIDEY WEB-SLING AT HIGH SPEEDS THROUGH THE CITY, CONFIDENT THAT HE WON'T FALL.

BULLET DODGING
SPIDEY'S SPIDER-SENSE PLUS REFLEXES MEAN HE CAN AVOID GUN FIRE BEFORE HE EVEN HAS A CHANCE TO THINK ABOUT IT!

UNDETECTABLE
THE SPIDER-SENSE DOESN'T WORK ON VENOM, BECAUSE ITS ALIEN SYMBIOTE WAS ONCE MENTALLY LINKED TO SPIDEY.

IN THE DARK
THANKS TO THE SPIDER-SENSE SPIDEY CAN NAVIGATE DARKENED ROOMS, AVOIDING HAZARDS AND NOISY OBJECTS THAT MAY GIVE HIM AWAY.

FAST FACTS SPIDER-MAN

ASTONISHING ENEMIES
Doctor Octopus, the Lizard, Electro... Spidey's rogues' gallery is second to none!

SPIDER-VERSIONS
There's not just one Spidey! Countless arachnid heroes exist across the strands of the Spider-Verse!

MIGHTY MATES
He used to fight alone, but did you know that Spider-Man's now a fully fledged member of the Avengers?

IRON ARMOUR
Tony Stark once designed Spidey his own 'Iron Spider' suit... complete with robotic arms!

SUPERIOR SPIDER
Doctor Octopus once took over as Spidey... vowing to become an even more amazing arachnid Avenger!

TRAINING DAY

SCRIPT: FERG HANDLEY   PENCILS: CARLOS GOMEZ   INKS: GARY ERSKINE
COLOURS: JAMES OFFREDI   LETTERING: WILL LUCAS

THE NERVE OF THE GUY. THAT'S THE THIRD WEEK *RUNNIN'* HE'S BEEN LATE WITH HIS PROTECTION MONEY.

WELL WE GOT IT NOW, PLUS INTEREST. AN' THAT'S OUR LAST CALL, SO WHAT SAY WE...

THAT'S FAR ENOUGH. HAND IT OVER, AN' DON'T TRY ANYTHIN' SMART.

YER KIDDIN', RIGHT?

YEAH, THIS IS *SILVERMANE'S* PAYOLA. SO GET OUTTA HERE!

SILVERMANE'S FINISHED, FAT MAN. FROM NOW ON, HAMMERHEAD'S CREW ARE RUNNIN' THE SHOW.

AN' JUST SO YOUSE GET THE MESSAGE...

FWAAK

UNFF!

UNLUCKY, FELLAS.

WHO THE...?

KA-BOOM!

SONOVAGUN! HALF A SEC SLOWER AND THAT WOULD'VE TAKEN MY HEAD OFF!

AND THERE THEY GO, DANG IT.

HOLD IT *RIGHT* THERE!

YEP, ASSAULT AND ROBBERY -- YOU'RE GOING DOWN FOR THIS, WALLCRAWLER!

SORRY BOYS, BUT I CAN'T DO THIS RIGHT NOW!

FWIPP

FWIPP

SEE, I *TOLD* YOU HE WAS NO GOOD.

YOU AND JONAH JAMESON BOTH, MIKE.

UNREAL. ALL I EVER DO IS FIGHT CRIME -- AND THERE'S STILL COPS WHO THINK I'M A BAD GUY.

ANYHOW, I HEARD ONE OF THOSE GRUNTS MENTION HAMMERHEAD. SO THE NEXT NIGHT, I HEAD OVER TO SOUTH BROOKLYN...

...AND THE SCUZZY BAR HE USES AS AN HQ.

PLACE CLOSES AT MIDNIGHT, HE'S THERE BY TEN PAST. AND THE WAY HE'S TALKING, HE MUST'VE HAD THE ROOM SWEPT FOR BUGS...

WITH THE KINGPIN IN THE SLAMMER, THIS CITY'S WIDE OPEN. AN' AFTER TONIGHT, NOBODY'S GONNA MESS WITH US.

WORD ON THAT, BOSS.

Y'KNOW, I WASN'T SURE ABOUT THAT FANCY MARTIAL ARTS STUFF. BUT THOSE MOOKS A' SILVERMANE'S WENT DOWN LIKE THAT!

OKAY, I'VE HEARD ENOUGH. GANG WARFARE, KUNG-FU KICKING HOODS...

...TIME TO NIP THIS THING IN THE BUD.

DARN IT, SPIDER-MAN, YOU'RE GOING TO RUIN EVERYTHING.

THE WALLCRAWLER!

EASY, PINHEADS. I JUST WANT A WORD WITH YOUR BOSS, THAT'S ALL.

YOU'VE GOT THIRTY SECONDS, PUNK, SO START YAPPING.

OKAY, HERE'S THE SHORT VERSION. I DIDN'T HELP PUT THE KINGPIN AWAY FOR YOU TO START A GANG WAR.

SO, WHATEVER YOU'RE PLANNING, FORGET ABOUT IT. THERE, *SHORT* ENOUGH FOR YOU?

BOYS, PUT THE HURT ON THIS CREEP.

NOW YER *TALKIN',* BOSS!

THIS SHOULDN'T BE A CONTEST. BUT THE FIVE AMIGOS HERE ARE PRETTY SLICK...

...AND THEY DEFINITELY KNOW HOW TO USE THEIR WEAPONS.

...SO I DO WHAT I DO...

STILL, IT ISN'T LIKE THEY'VE GOT SUPERPOWERS OR SUCHLIKE...

THWAAK

SMACK

...AND THAT'S ALL SHE WROTE. SO, LET'S SEE IF OLD FLAT TOP'S STILL...

HMM, NOW LET ME SEE. ADAMANTIUM BONCE, ADAMANTIUM SHIELD... THAT'S GONNA BE SOME CLANG ALRIGHT.

NO IT AIN'T, WALLCRAWLER. I'M CALLING TIME ON THIS, SEE...BUT ONLY 'COS YOUSE GOT ME OUTNUMBERED.

ANYHOW, YOU JOKERS DON'T HAVE NUTHIN' ON ME. SO GO ON, BEAT IT.

THREE WORDS, CAP. HEAD AND SHIELD.

NO, HE'S RIGHT SPIDER-MAN. EVEN IF WE TOOK HIM IN, WE DON'T HAVE A SHRED OF EVIDENCE.

YEAH? WELL I'LL BE WATCHING YOU, HAMMERHEAD...SO STEP OUT OF LINE, AND YOU'LL BE SHARING AN EIGHT BY TWELVE WITH THE KINGPIN!

THAT TOLD HIM.

MAYBE. BUT IT WON'T MAKE ANY DIFFERENCE.

18

HEH. GOT THAT RIGHT, YA PAIR OF DEADBEATS.

FRESH AIR FEELS GOOD AFTER THAT DIVE. SO WE DO THE ROOFTOP THING...

...AND I FIND OUT THAT CAP HAD GOTTEN A TIP-OFF FROM AN OLD INFORMANT, AND THAT HE'D BEEN ON THE CASE FOR A WHILE NOW...

...WHICH IS HOW I LEARNED ABOUT A HIT ON *THE OWL'S* HEADQUARTERS -- AIMED AT TAKING OUT HIS ENTIRE GANG.

SO, I WAS PLANNING ON CATCHING THEM IN THE ACT. AND WITH HIS THUGS IN JAIL, HAMMERHEAD WOULD'VE BEEN BACK TO SQUARE ONE.

MY BAD THEN, CAP. LOOKS LIKE I REALLY SCREWED THINGS UP FOR YOU.

FORGET IT, SPIDEY. YOU WEREN'T TO KNOW... AND AT LEAST I CAN TAKE TASKMASTER IN FOR PAROLE VIOLATION.

I GUESS. SO WE'RE COOL THEN, RIGHT?

WE ARE, AND OFF WE HEAD. GOTTA SAY THOUGH, THIS GANG WAR STUFF HAS GOTTEN ME WORRIED.

IN FACT, THINGS WERE EASIER WHEN THE KINGPIN WAS CONTROLLING THE CITY. AT LEAST...

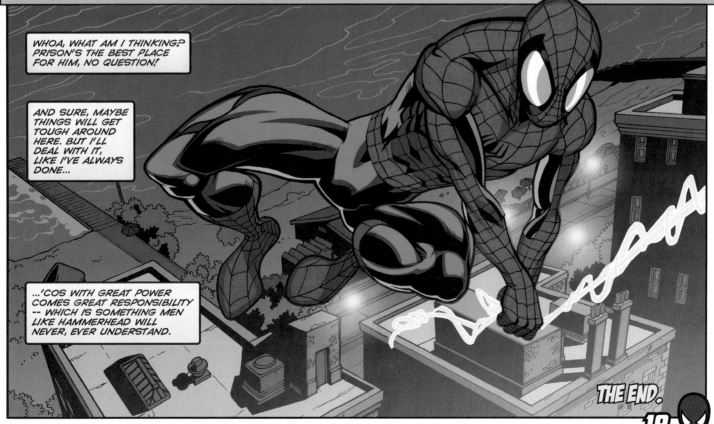

WHOA, WHAT AM I THINKING? PRISON'S THE BEST PLACE FOR HIM, NO QUESTION!

AND SURE, MAYBE THINGS WILL GET TOUGH AROUND HERE. BUT I'LL DEAL WITH IT, LIKE I'VE ALWAYS DONE...

...'COS WITH GREAT POWER COMES GREAT RESPONSIBILITY -- WHICH IS SOMETHING MEN LIKE HAMMERHEAD WILL NEVER, EVER UNDERSTAND.

THE END.

19

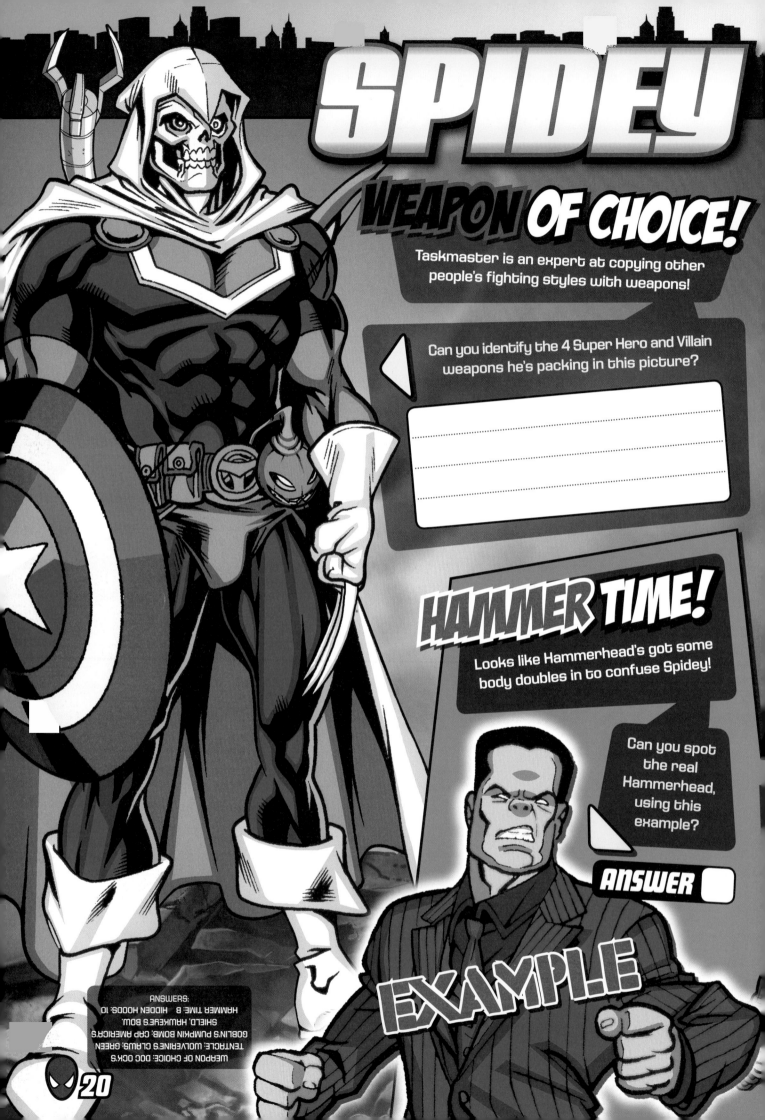

SPIDEY

WEAPON OF CHOICE!

Taskmaster is an expert at copying other people's fighting styles with weapons!

Can you identify the 4 Super Hero and Villain weapons he's packing in this picture?

HAMMER TIME!

Looks like Hammerhead's got some body doubles in to confuse Spidey!

Can you spot the real Hammerhead, using this example?

ANSWER

EXAMPLE

CENTRAL!

How many can you spot in this picture?

HIDDEN HOODS!

Some more of Hammerhead's hoods are trying to sneak up on Spidey!

HOW MANY HOODS DID YOU FIND?

A
B
C
D
E
F
G
H

21

COLOUR!

SPIDER FILE

DOCTOR CURT CONNORS ISN'T THE ONLY MEDICAL MARVELITE OUT THERE. HERE'S WHO WE WOULD AND WOULDN'T WANT TREATING US IF WE WERE ILL...

CALL A

DOCTOR STRANGE

DR STEPHEN STRANGE WAS A TALENTED NEUROSURGEON, UNTIL A CAR ACCIDENT DAMAGED THE NERVES IN HIS HANDS, ENDING HIS SURGICAL CAREER. FORTUNATELY, STRANGE WAS ALSO DESTINED TO BECOME THE NEXT SORCERER SUPREME, AND AN EXPERT IN THE MYSTIC ARTS.

Qualifications

Medical doctorate; extensive sorcery training

POSITIVES
One of the most powerful sorcerers in existence.

NEGATIVES
Needs magic to supplement his damaged hands in surgery.

DOCTOR DOOM

A MASTER OF SORCERY FROM A YOUNG AGE, AND A SCIENTIFIC GENIUS AS A TEENAGER, VICTOR VON DOOM IS AS EVIL AS HE IS SMART. DRESSED IN AN ARMOURED SUIT, HE WILL STOP AT NOTHING IN HIS QUEST FOR ULTIMATE POWER.

Qualifications

Self-educated genius in science and mystic arts, but expelled from college

POSITIVES
One of the cleverest people in the Marvel Universe.

NEGATIVES
No official qualifications... oh, and he's an evil, diabolical Super Villain!

DOCTOR!

DOCTOR CONNORS

DR CURT CONNORS LOST HIS RIGHT ARM IN A BATTLEFIELD BLAST WHEN HE WAS AN ARMY SURGEON. HE CREATED A SERUM TO GROW IT BACK, WHICH WORKED, BUT ALSO TURNED HIM INTO A REPTILIAN MONSTER WITH A COMPLETELY SEPARATE AND SAVAGE PERSONALITY.

Qualifications

Medical school graduate; twin doctorates in biology and biochemistry

POSITIVES

Erm, he managed to grow his right arm back? That's pretty impressive!

NEGATIVES

Any hint of stress and he could turn into a giant ferocious lizard monster. Not good!

DOCTOR OCTOPUS

DR OTTO OCTAVIUS WAS A BRILLIANT ATOMIC RESEARCHER, UNTIL A FREAK ACCIDENT IN THE LAB BOMBARDED HIM WITH RADIATION, GRAFTING FOUR MECHANICAL TENTACLE-LIKE ARMS TO HIS BACK, AND CHANGING HIM INTO A POWER-HUNGRY SUPER CRIMINAL.

Qualifications

Ph.D. in nuclear physics

POSITIVES

Those extra arms really would come in handy for complex operations.

NEGATIVES

Has a nasty habit of trying to take over the world now and again.

25

EMPIRE STATE UNIVERSITY. THE LABORATORY OF DOCTOR *CURT CONNORS*...

MAN, THERE MUST BE A *HUNDRED* DEMONSTRATORS OUTSIDE, PROTESTING THE NEW TUITION HIKES. NOT THAT I BLAME THEM, BUT...

DOCTOR CONNORS? HEY, ARE YOU *ALL RIGHT*?

BIG LIZARD ON CAMPUS

PETER? IT'S... NOTHING. JUST A *PHANTOM PAIN* FROM MY MISSING ARM. I STILL GET IT FROM TIME TO TIME.

WELL, IF YOU'RE SURE THAT'S ALL IT IS.

REALLY, I'M FI —

NNYAHHH!!

YOU DON'T *SOUND* FINE! WHY DON'T WE —?

NO! GET *OUT*, PARKER!

HEY —!

SLAM

HE SHOVED ME OUT LIKE I WAS A 98-POUND WEAKLING! THIS IS MOST DEFINITELY *NOT* GOOD!

340

DOC CONNORS DOESN'T KNOW *MY* SECRET —

PENCILS: JOHN ROYLE INKS: DAVID ROACH COLOURS: JAMES OFFREDI SCRIPT: ROGER STERN LETTERS: PERI GODBOLD

— BUT I KNOW *HIS!* AND FROM THE WAY MY SPIDER-SENSE IS BUZZIN' —

MUST BE THAT NEW SERUM I TRIED EARLIER - SOME SORT OF DELAYED REACTION....

NEED THE *ANTIDOTE...!*

"- HE NEEDS MORE HELP THAN PETER PARKER CAN GIVE HIM!"

POOR GUY, ALL HE WANTED WAS TO HELP HIMSELF AND OTHER AMPUTEES —

—TO FIND A WAY TO REGENERATE LOST LIMBS!

ARGH!

HIS RESEARCH INTO REPTILIAN DNA GAVE HIM HIS ARM BACK... BUT THERE WAS ONE BAD SIDE EFFECT!

TOO LATE!

THE CHANGE HAS BEGUN!

WE'RE BOTH THE RESULTS OF SCIENTIFIC ACCIDENTS. I BECAME SPIDER-MAN AND HE BECAME A MONSTER CALLED...

"...*THE LIZARD!*"

I LIVE AGAIN!

CONNORS PLANNED TO STOP ME WITH HIS ACCURSED SERUMS —

27

LOOK OUT!

RUN!

KRUNCH

KEEP AWAY, MAMMALS! SPIDER-MAN IS *MINE!*

911! CALL 911!

KRACK

NOT SO FAST, TALL, GREEN AND GRUESOME!

DON'T FOCUS ON ME! GET THE ACTION!

WE'RE GOING LIVE IN THREE...TWO...

Missed me!

AT THAT MOMENT, INSIDE A SILO ON NEARBY STATEN ISLAND...

HOME AT LAST, THANKS TO SPIDER-MAN'S DISREGARD FOR POLICE PROCEDURE, AND A GOOD LAWYER...

... I MEAN, DID THAT WALL-CRAWLING PEST REALLY THINK HE'D GET AWAY WITH 'ASSAULTING' ME THE WAY THAT HE DID?*

...ON THE ESU CAMPUS, WHERE SPIDER-MAN IS IN A FIGHT FOR HIS LIFE —

EH?

*SPIDEY AND THE VULTURE FACED-OFF IN ISSUE 210 OF SPECTACULAR SPIDER-MAN.

— AFTER APPARENTLY BEING THROWN THROUGH THE SIDE OF A NEARBY BUILDING BY THE LIZARD!

ALLEZ-OOP!

LITTLE IS KNOWN ABOUT THE MYSTERIOUS LIZARD WHO HAS OFTEN BEEN DISMISSED AS AN *URBAN LEGEND*

— BUT AS YOU CAN SEE —!

HEY, GET BACK! IT'S NOT SAFE —!

SLAAAAM

AH-HAH-HA!

NOW THAT DOES MY HEART GOOD! IF ONLY *I* WAS THE ONE HITTING HIM —!

OH!

FWIPP

HEY! HANDS OFF THE MEDIA, SCALY!

YOU HAVE ENOUGH TO WORRY ABOUT FROM ME!

NOW GIDDY-UP! I WANNA PONY RIDE!

WHEN I GET FREE OF THIS WEBBING, I'LL FLAY THE FLESH FROM YOUR BONES!

BOY, HOW RUDE!

AND HERE I AM, NICE ENOUGH TO STEER YOU AROUND HARD OBJECTS!

GOT TO GET YOU FAR AWAY FROM INNOCENT BYSTANDERS —

—AND PRYING EYES — BEFORE MY WEBBING BREAKS DOWN! I JUST NEED A FEW MINUTES TO ADMINISTER THE ANTIDOTE.

AH! THIS LITTLE CUL-DE-SAC SHOULD DO THE TRICK!

C'MON, LIZ, STOP SPINNING 'ROUND!

THAT'S IT, OPEN UP AND SAY —!

H-HALT! STOP OR I'LL —!!

SMASH

OH, NO!

HOLD YOUR FIRE!

THE LIZARD'S PRACTICALLY BULLETPROOF —

— BUT I'M NOT!

S-SPIDER-MAN?! DIDN'T SEE YOU BACK THERE —!

GET DOWN!!

ANY CLOSER, AND NEITHER OF US WOULD EVER NEED HATS AGAIN!

WHOOPS! 'SCUSE ME, OFFICER! THERE'S A MAN I GOTTA CATCH!

A MAN —?

WELL, HE USED TO BE...

I'D FORGOTTEN HOW FAST THE LIZARD CAN MOVE. THESE TUNNELS GO ON FOR MILES!

I HAVE TO FIND THAT MONSTER BEFORE I CAN SAVE THE MAN INSIDE, AND I HAVE TO DO IT SOON — BEFORE HE HURTS HIMSELF OR SOMEONE ELSE.

YEAH, THAT'S ALL...

I'M STANDING HERE IN A LITTLE-TRAVELED ALLEYWAY NEAR THE CAMPUS OF EMPIRE STATE UNIVERSITY. AT MY FEET — AN OPEN MANHOLE.

WE'RE NOW TOLD THAT SPIDER-MAN SURFACED HERE, LESS THAN AN HOUR AGO, AFTER CHASING THE MYSTERIOUS LIZARD INTO THE SEWERS OF MANHATTAN EARLIER TODAY.

WHERE SPIDER-MAN WENT — AND WHAT HE DID — IS ANYONE'S GUESS. BUT WE DO KNOW THAT *ESU* HAS SEEN ITS SHARE OF MAYHEM IN THE PAST 48 HOURS! THIS AFTERNOON, AN OTHERWISE PEACEFUL DEMONSTRATION WAS DISRUPTED —

"— BY SPIDER-MAN AND THE LIZARD. THEIR BATTLE WRECKED THE LABORATORY OF DOCTOR CURTIS CONNORS, AND THEN RAGED ACROSS CAMPUS!

AUTHORITIES HAVE SO FAR BEEN UNABLE TO LOCATE CONNORS, AND THERE'S BEEN NO FURTHER SIGN OF THE LIZARD —

"— BUT POLICE REPORT THAT SPIDER-MAN WAS SEEN RE-ENTERING THE SEWERS..."

I'D HOPED THAT THE LIZARD HAD SNUCK BACK TO CONNORS' LAB...

I OUGHT TO HAVE MY HEAD EXAMINED FOR COMING BACK DOWN HERE — BUT I DON'T HAVE MUCH CHOICE!

...BUT I FOUND NO SIGN OF HIM THERE — WHICH MAY MEAN THAT HE'S REJECTING MORE AND MORE OF HIS HUMAN IDENTITY... NOT GOOD...

...NOT GOOD AT ALL! I HAVE TO PICK UP THE LIZARD'S TRAIL...

...AND TRY TO TURN HIM BACK INTO DOCTOR CONNORS BEFORE IT'S TOO LATE.

WHOA! WHO FLUSHED?

SPLOSH

MOTHER NATURE, DUMMY! THERE'S A REASON THIS IS CALLED A *STORM* SEWER!

RAIN MUST BE PICKING UP. THAT'S JUST DANDY...

"...HOW COULD THINGS GET ANY WORSE?"

MOVE ALONG... NOTHIN' TO SEE HERE!

QUITE RIGHT, OFFICER —

— THE REAL ACTION IS OBVIOUSLY UNDERGROUND.

I'VE NEVER HAD THE PLEASURE OF MEETING THE LIZARD... PERHAPS THIS EVENING WILL PROVIDE THE OPPORTUNITY FOR A NEW ALLIANCE!

PHEW! STORM SEWERS OR NOT, THE STUFF THAT'S FLOWING AROUND HERE STILL ISN'T EXACTLY *EVIAN!*

I'VE BEEN IN FISH MARKETS THAT SMELLED FRESHER!

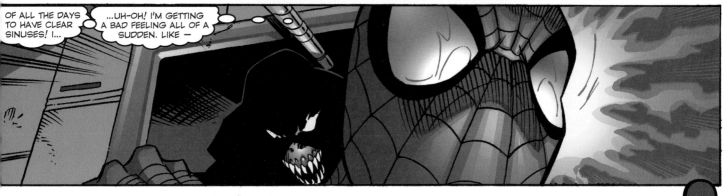

OF ALL THE DAYS TO HAVE CLEAR SINUSES! I...

...UH-OH! I'M GETTING A BAD FEELING ALL OF A SUDDEN. LIKE —

— I'M DEFINITELY NOT ALONE!

BLESS YOU, LI'L SPIDER-SENSES!

THAT WAS CLOSE, THOUGH! A LITTLE SLOWER, AND I'D BE SINGING SOPRANO.

BETTER WRAP LIZ UP —!

FWIPP **FWIPP**

OH, *NO!* DON'T TELL ME —!

WEB-SHOOTERS CLOGGED, SPIDER-MAN? TOO BAD FOR YOU!

HEY, LET'S NOT DO ANYTHING RASH!

DOCTOR CONNORS, LISTEN TO ME! I KNOW YOU'RE IN THERE —!

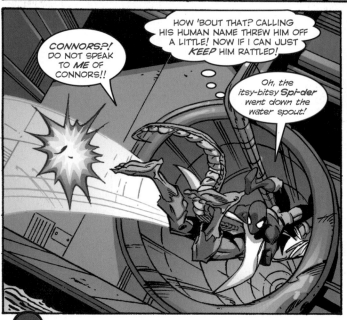

CONNORS?! DO NOT SPEAK TO *ME* OF CONNORS!!

HOW 'BOUT THAT? CALLING HIS HUMAN NAME THREW HIM OFF A LITTLE! NOW IF I CAN JUST *KEEP* HIM RATTLED!

Oh, the itsy-bitsy Spi-der went down the water spout!

Jumped on a lizard, and soon they both slid —

— OW!

THOKK

OH, BOY...

"...THIS IS BAD."

SURPRISED, SPIDER-MAN? YOUR LITTLE UNDERGROUND ESCAPADE IS ALL OVER THE MEDIA. MY FINDING YOU WAS CHILD'S PLAY!

GREETINGS, LIZARD! I AM THE VULTURE. I JUST DROPPED IN TO LEND —

— A HELPING HAND!

SPLOSH

EH?! DON'T ATTACK ME —

— I CAME HERE TO HELP YOU DESTROY SPIDER-MAN!

KRACK

RIP

ARROGANT FOOL! THE LIZARD NEEDS NO HELP!

AND I DON'T LIKE BIRD-MEN ANY MORE THAN I DO SPIDER-MEN!

HU-UK-K-K!

THIS LIZARD EATS BIRDS!

NOT SO FAST, SCALY!

SPIDER-MAN? ALIVE?!

YEAH, NO THANKS TO YOU!

STRUGGLE WITH HIM JUST A FEW MORE SECONDS, VULCH — THIS WON'T TAKE LONG...

?

...I HOPE! I FOUND THIS EXTRA VIAL OF ANTIDOTE IN DOC CONNOR'S LAB, BUT WHO KNOWS IF IT'S STILL GOOD OR NOT?

UNNGH!

YOU TRIED TO POISON ME?!

HE... HE THREW ME AWAY... AS IF I WAS NOTHING!

AND SPIDER-MAN USED ME!!

OW! THANKS A LOT, VULTCH!

REMIND ME NOT TO SAVE YOUR NECK NEXT TIME...

...IF THERE IS A NEXT TIME! THIS IS JUST GREAT —

FWOOOSH

"— IT'S NOT ENOUGH THAT I HAVE TO DEAL WITH THE LIZARD AND THE VULTURE! OF COURSE, A WALL WOULD HAVE TO GIVE WAY —

— WITH MY LUCK, HOW COULD IT *NOT*?

HELP ME!

I CAN'T SWIM!!

SORRY, VULTCH — CAN'T SNAG YOU WITHOUT MY WEBBING!

IT'S ALL I CAN DO... TO HANG ON TO... THE LIZARD...

...IN THIS DELUGE!

OPEN AIR! JUST IN TIME!

KOFF-KOFF!

YOU OKAY, DOC?

SPIDER-MAN? I... THINK SO. WHAT HAPPENED —?

LONG STORY...

...AND WHEN THE WALL GAVE WAY, THE LIZARD WAS STUNNED BY A CHUNK OF DEBRIS.

WHAT ABOUT THE VULTURE? WAS HE —?

SWEPT AWAY.

THEN... I AS GOOD AS KILLED HIM.

NO WAY, DOC! THE VULTURE BROUGHT THAT ON HIMSELF. BESIDES, HE'S TOUGH, I DOUBT HE DROWNED.

I SEE. I... ...I OWE YOU EVERYTHING, SPIDER-MAN. YOU STOPPED THE LIZARD, YOU SAVED MY LIFE —!

HEY, ALL PART OF THE JOB, DOC. NOW PUT ON YOUR THINKING CAP...

...WE STILL HAVE TO DO DECIDE WHAT TO TELL THE MEDIA!

THE END.

MIXING IT UP!

SPIDEY'S TRYING TO MAKE MORE ANTIDOTE IN CASE HE LOSES THE STUFF HE'S GOT.

ADD THE GREEN LIQUID SECOND.

ADD THE PURPLE LIQUID DIRCTLY BEFORE THE BLUE.

ADD THE YELLOW LIQUID AFTER THE GREEN.

ADD THE BLUE LIQUID LAST.

ADD THE RED LIQUID BEFORE THE GREEN LIQUID.

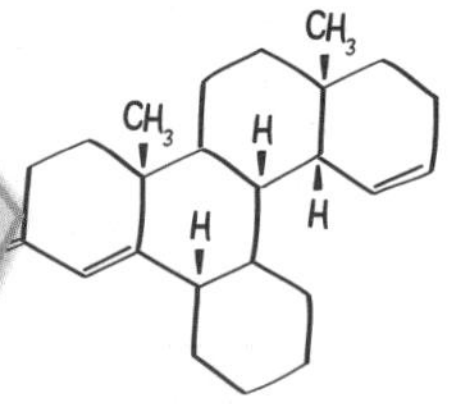

CAN YOU USE DR CONNORS' NOTES TO WORK OUT WHICH ORDER TO MIX THE COLOURED LIQUIDS IN?

RAT RACE!

FINDING LIZARD'S GOING TO BE TRICKY IN THIS MAZE OF SEWER TUNNELS.

FINISH

CAN YOU WORK OUT THE ROUTE THAT LEADS FROM SPIDEY TO LIZARD?

START

CENTRAL!

SHADOW LURKER!

SPIDEY KNOWS THE LIZARD'S DOWN IN THE SEWERS SOMEWHERE, BUT IS HAVING A TOUGH TIME FINDING HIM.

CAN YOU HELP BY SPOTTING THE SCALY TERROR IN EACH OF THE PICTURES BELOW?

ANIMAL SPOTTING!

THE LIZARD'S NOT THE ONLY MARVEL CHARACTER NAMED AFTER AN ANIMAL.

CAN YOU FIND ALL OF THE ANIMAL-BASED MARVELITES LISTED IN THE WORD GRID BELOW?

- WOLVERINE ☐
- RHINO ☐   LIZARD ☐
- PUMA ☐   JACKAL ☐
- BEETLE ☐   OWL ☐
- KANGAROO ☐
- CHAMELEON ☐
- PORCUPINE ☐
- VULTURE ☐
- SCORPION ☐

```
C Y O G K I N S R T E D
H W S C O R P I O N T E D
A F D Z B T W U P O N L D L
M C W V A F M D M Q S I
E A W O Z I R P H A K X Z
L C V U L T U R E C U A
E K S T U V C A N V I R D
O A Y L D H E I Q U K P
N L F S E U G R H I N O
S W P O R C U P I N E W
M K A N G A R O O N M L
B E E T L E S H W G E L
```

39

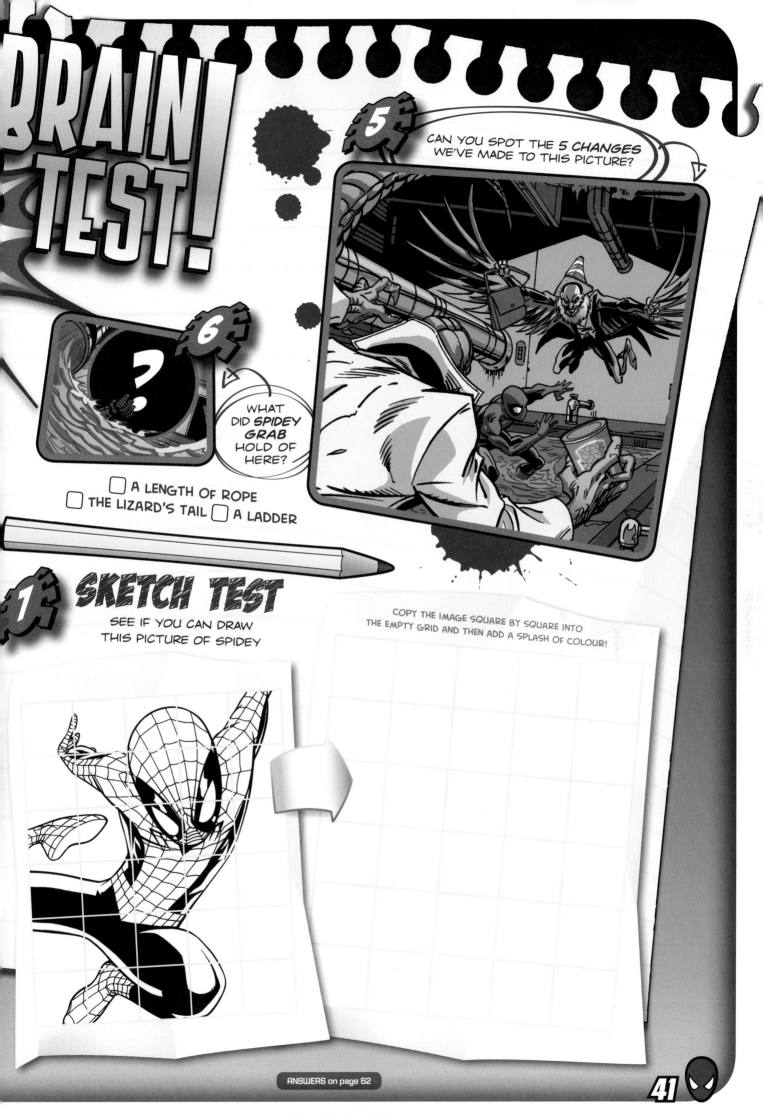

BRAIN TEST!

5 CAN YOU SPOT THE 5 CHANGES WE'VE MADE TO THIS PICTURE?

6 WHAT DID **SPIDEY** **GRAB** HOLD OF HERE?

☐ A LENGTH OF ROPE
☐ THE LIZARD'S TAIL ☐ A LADDER

1 SKETCH TEST

SEE IF YOU CAN DRAW THIS PICTURE OF SPIDEY

COPY THE IMAGE SQUARE BY SQUARE INTO THE EMPTY GRID AND THEN ADD A SPLASH OF COLOUR!

ANSWERS on page 62

BUILD YOUR OWN

LIZARD

FOLLOW THESE STEPS TO MAKE YOUR VERY OWN LIZARD DOOR HANGER FOR YOUR BEDROOM!

Step 1

Stick the opposite page to some card, then carefully cut out each of the sides of the door hanger.

Step 2

Stick the backs of each side together to make a double-sided hanger.

Step 3

Finally wrap the tail around a doorknob, making sure the message you want is facing away from the door!

FOOLISH MAMMALS! A MERE DOOR HANGER CANNOT STOP *THE LIZARD!*

PLEASE COME IN... IF YOU DARE!

DOOR HANGER

BE CAREFUL WHEN YOU'RE CUTTING OUT THE TEMPLATES - NOT EVERYONE HAS TOUGH, SCALY SKIN AND A HEALING FACTOR LIKE THE LIZARD!

MONSTER INSIDE... DO NOT DISTURB!

PLEASE COME IN... IF YOU DARE!

RIGHT, SPIDER FANS, IT'S TIME TO MEET ONE OF SPIDEY'S MOST BIG-HEADED FOES... AND WE DON'T MEAN OVER-CONFIDENT!

JACK

DISGRACED

JASON MACENDALE WAS RECRUITED FROM COLLEGE TO THE CIA, BEFORE HE WAS THROWN OUT BECAUSE OF HIS VIOLENT NATURE AND BRUTAL METHODS.

ANGER ISSUES

MACENDALE'S ANGER AT THE US GOVERNMENT FOR FIRING HIM LED HIM TO BECOME AN INTERNATIONAL MERCENARY AND CRIMINAL.

FLAME ON

TO PROMOTE HIS SERVICES TO EMPLOYERS, HE BEGAN DRESSING IN THE JACK O'LANTERN COSTUME (WHO'S GOING TO MISS A BIG, FLAMING PUMPKIN HEAD, RIGHT?!)

O'LANTERN

SPIDER FOE

JACK'S COSTUME ALSO BROUGHT HIM TO THE ATTENTION OF SPIDEY, AND THE TWO OF THEM HAVE BEEN BATTLING PUMPKIN-HEAD TO HEAD EVER SINCE!

TRICK OR TREAT?

JACK O'LANTERN'S MUCH MORE THAN JUST A BIG, FLAMING HEAD - CHECK OUT WHAT MAKES HIM SO DANGEROUS BELOW!

Bullet-proof helmet

Infa-red image sensors for seeing in the dark

Electric wrist blasters

Bazooka resistant body armour

Extensive combat and espionage training

Almost peak human strength, agility and endurance

Smoke, explosive and concussion grenades

Flying disk similar in speed to a goblin glider

OKAY, IT'S NOT EXACTLY GLAMOROUS. BUT FIGHTING CRIME SOMETIMES MEANS SURVEILLANCE WORK...

...WHICH IS WHY I'M LURKING AROUND OUTSIDE A SEEDY TENEMENT ON THE LOWER EAST SIDE.

THE GUY INSIDE IS JASON MACENDALE, BETTER KNOWN AS JACK O'LANTERN. AND SEEING AS HE'S A DANGEROUS SUPER VILLAIN JUST OUT ON PAROLE...

...I FIGURED IT'D BE A GOOD IDEA TO CHECK HIM OUT.

AN HOUR DRAGS BY, THEN ANOTHER. BUT JUST AS I DECIDE TO CALL IT A NIGHT, HE GETS A CALL...

YEAH, IT'S ME. AND NO, I HAVEN'T FORGOTTEN ABOUT THAT DOUGH I OWE YOU.

NOT ME, MACENDALE, THE KINGPIN. I'M JUST HELPING TAKE CARE OF BUSINESS WHILE HE'S INSIDE.

RELAX, ZANETTI, IT'S ALL IN HAND. END OF THE WEEK, WE'RE ALL SQUARED UP.

WE'D BETTER BE. AND DON'T FORGET, THE INTEREST'S A POINT A DAY.

TYPICAL. THE KINGPIN'S LOCKED UP ON REMAND, AND HE'S STILL RAKING IT IN.

STILL, IT DOESN'T LOOK LIKE ANYTHING'S GOING TO HAPPEN TONIGHT. SO WHEN HE'S IN THE OTHER ROOM...

BLIND JUSTICE

PENCILS: JOHN ROYLE
INKS: PHILIP MOY
COLOURS: JAMES OFFREDI
SCRIPT: FERG HANDLEY

THERE. THE SPIDER-TRACER WILL HELP ME KEEP TABS ON HIM, MEANING I CAN FINALLY HEAD HOME FOR SOME SHUTEYE.

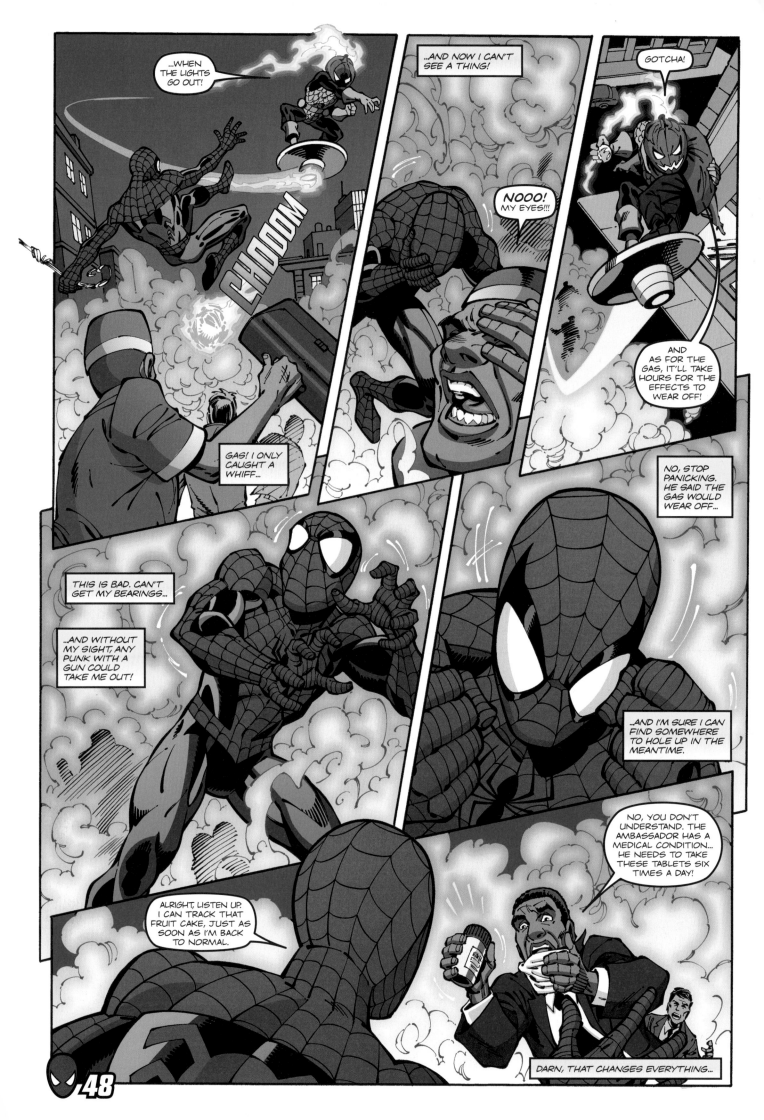

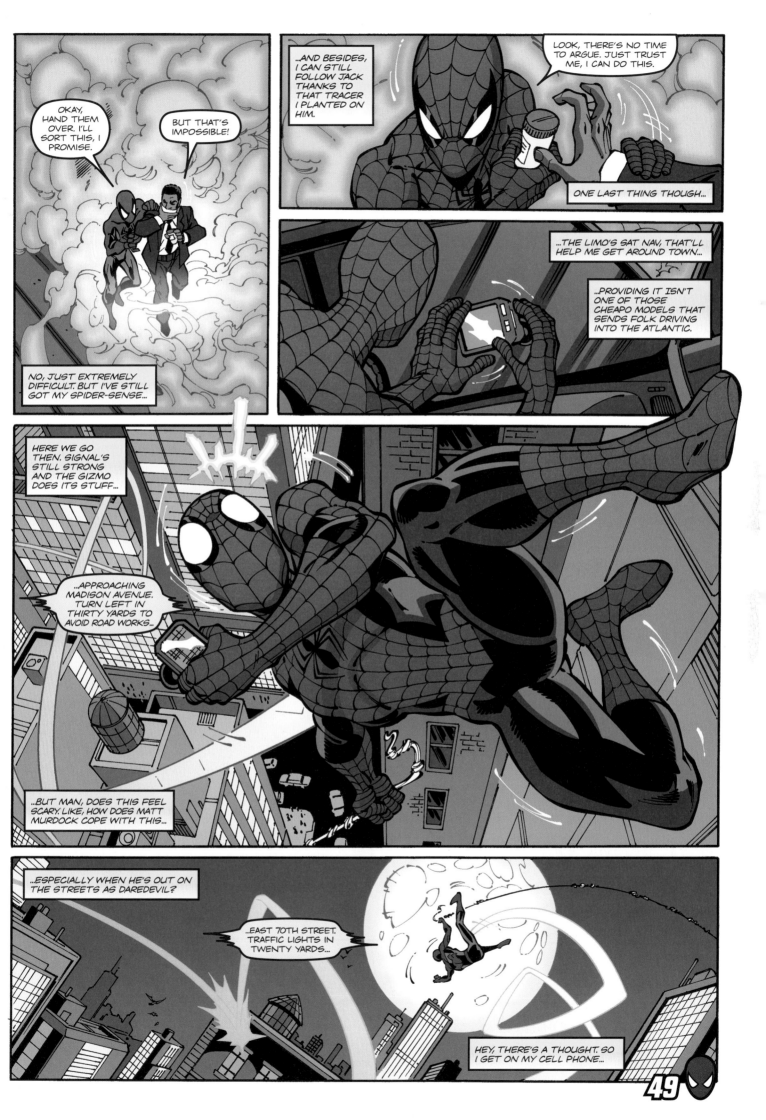

OKAY, HAND THEM OVER. I'LL SORT THIS, I PROMISE.

BUT THAT'S IMPOSSIBLE!

NO, JUST EXTREMELY DIFFICULT. BUT I'VE STILL GOT MY SPIDER-SENSE...

...AND BESIDES, I CAN STILL FOLLOW JACK TO THAT TRACER I PLANTED ON HIM.

LOOK, THERE'S NO TIME TO ARGUE. JUST TRUST ME, I CAN DO THIS.

ONE LAST THING THOUGH...

...THE LIMO'S SAT NAV, THAT'LL HELP ME GET AROUND TOWN...

...PROVIDING IT ISN'T ONE OF THOSE CHEAPO MODELS THAT SENDS FOLK DRIVING INTO THE ATLANTIC.

HERE WE GO THEN. SIGNAL'S STILL STRONG AND THE GIZMO DOES ITS STUFF...

...APPROACHING MADISON AVENUE. TURN LEFT IN THIRTY YARDS TO AVOID ROAD WORKS...

...BUT MAN, DOES THIS FEEL SCARY. LIKE, HOW DOES MATT MURDOCK COPE WITH THIS...

...ESPECIALLY WHEN HE'S OUT ON THE STREETS AS DAREDEVIL?

...EAST 70TH STREET. TRAFFIC LIGHTS IN TWENTY YARDS...

HEY, THERE'S A THOUGHT. SO I GET ON MY CELL PHONE...

49

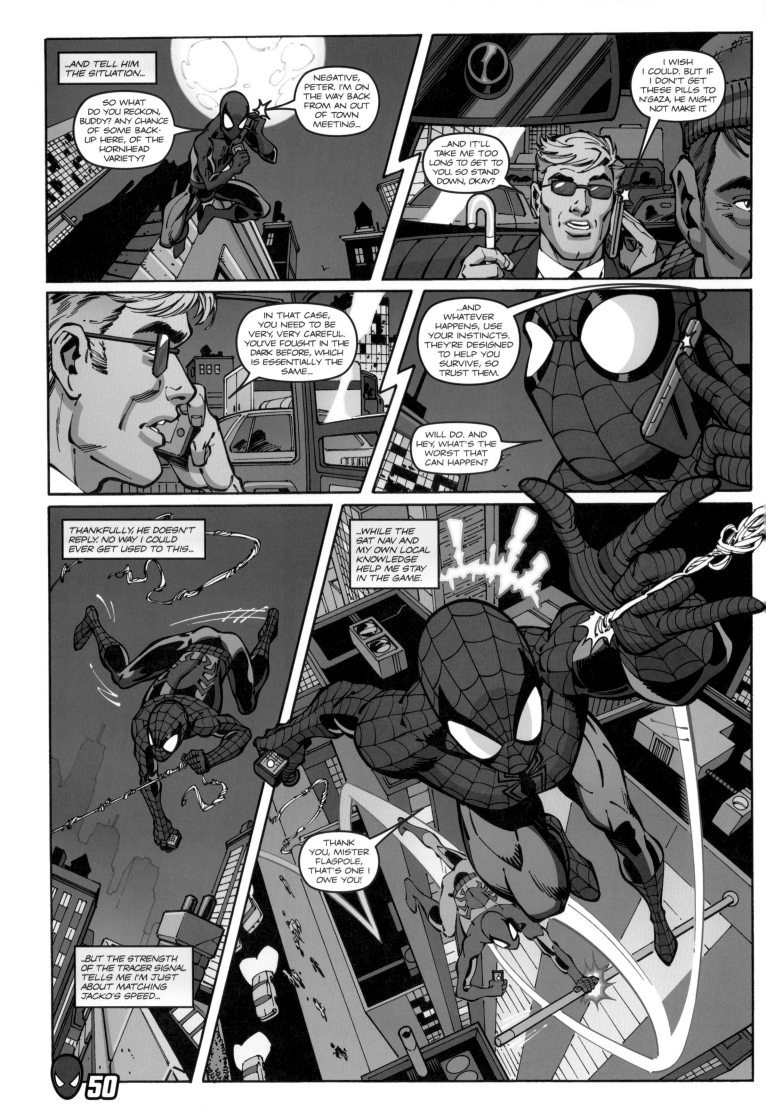

BRAIN TEST!

5 WHAT ARE THE 5 CHANGES WE'VE MADE TO THIS PICTURE?

6 WHAT WAS JACK O'LANTERN REALLY SAYING HERE?

HEH, JUST LIKE SHOOTING FISH IN A BARREL.

JUST 'COS YA CAN'T SEE THIS, DOESN'T MEAN IT WON'T HURT!

THIS MAY COME AS A SHOCK TO YOU, WALLCRAWLER!

7 SKETCH TEST

SEE IF YOU CAN DRAW THIS PICTURE OF JACK O'LANTERN!

COPY THE IMAGE SQUARE BY SQUARE INTO THE EMPTY GRID AND THEN ADD A SPLASH OF COLOUR!

ANSWERS on page 62

SPIDEY

BLIND FAITH!

ANSWERS:

BLIND FAITH: ROUTE D (route on page 62)
PUMPKIN FACE: HEAD D
WHO'S THERE?:1. DOC OCK; 2. KRAVEN; 3. GREEN GOBLIN; 4. KINGPIN; 5. VENOM; 6. VULTURE

ANSWERS

SPIDEY CENTRAL!

RAT RACE!

SHADOW LURKER!

ANIMAL SPOTTING!

SPIDEY'S BRAIN TEST!

EYE SPIDEY!

SPIDEY'S BRAIN TEST!

BLIND FAITH!